Aggie and Matthew's Cool Tzatziki Dip

Aggie and Matthew's house

Dr Kapoor's house

Mrs Taylor's flat

Dr Kapoor's Spicy Indian Samosas

Mrs Taylor's Cheesy Owls

Grandpa's house

Grandpa's Delicious Spinach and Egg Tart

Katy's house

Stefan's house

Katy's Yummy Banana Cup Cakes

D1581242

Great thanks to friends and family for
trying out all the recipes and to
The Big Lunch team for their great support.
JE   LHR

GEORGE AND FLORA'S BIG PARTY
AN EDEN PROJECT BOOK 978 1 905 81187 8
Published in Great Britain by Eden Project Books,
an imprint of Random House Children's Books
A Random House Group Company
This edition published 2012

1 3 5 7 9 10 8 6 4 2

Text copyright © Jo Elworthy, 2012
Illustrations copyright © Ley Honor Roberts, 2012
The right of Jo Elworthy and Ley Honor Roberts to be identified as the author and illustrator of
this work has been asserted in accordance with the Copyright, Designs and Patents Act 1988.

Eden Project Books are published by Random House Children's Books,
61–63 Uxbridge Road, London W5 5SA

www.kidsatrandomhouse.co.uk
www.edenproject.com
www.totallyrandombooks.co.uk
www.randomhouse.co.uk

Addresses for companies within The Random House Group Limited can be found at:
www.randomhouse.co.uk/offices.htm
THE RANDOM HOUSE GROUP Limited Reg. No. 954009
The Eden Project, owned by the Eden Trust, is an environmental education charity no. 1093070
CIP catalogue record for this book is available from the British Library.
Printed and bound in China

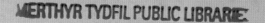
George and Flora's Big Party

Dear reader,

Hi. In this book we've collected loads of party recipes for you to try out. Each one lists enough ingredients to feed four people (unless it says otherwise). Grandpa said to tell you to wash your hands before you start and ask an adult to help with any cutting and hot cooking.
He also said something about washing up. Hmmm.

Anyway we hope you enjoy making and sharing these party foods. We certainly did.

Happy cooking,

George and Flora.

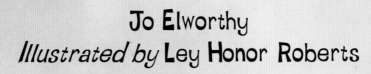

Jo Elworthy

Illustrated by **Ley Honor Roberts**

Eden Project Books

It was a lovely spring morning but poor Mum had a broken arm. George and Flora decided to help her with the cooking by making jam tarts.

"Hmmm, mine are a bit burnt," said George.
"Oops, mine are a bit soggy," added Flora.
"Grandpa is a great cook, maybe he could give you some tips when you go and see him tomorrow?" suggested Mum.

Grandpa showed Flora how to make pastry while
George looked for cooking ingredients in the garden.
"How about this?" asked George.
"Perfect," replied Grandpa. "We'll make an egg and spinach tart."
"Can we take some eggs home for Mum?" asked Flora.

"Of course," replied Grandpa. "I promised some to my friends Mr and Mrs Brown too. Can you pop them in to their house on your way home?"

Grandpa's Delicious Spinach and Egg Tart

Ingredients

Pastry	Filling
200 g plain flour	3 to 4 eggs
100 g margarine or butter	180 ml creamy milk
About 45 ml cold water	A handful of spinach (chopped)
A pinch of salt	
Flour for rolling out	23 cm flan dish

What to do

1. Sift flour into a cold bowl. Add salt.
2. Gently rub the butter into the flour until it looks like breadcrumbs.
3. Gradually add water (you may not need it all). Gently mix with your hands until you get a stiff dough.
4. Roll out the dough on a floured board.
5. Put into a greased flan dish. Bake in the oven at 200°C, gas mark 6 for 8 min.
   Tip: put some dried beans in the pastry case to stop the pastry puffing up.
6. Mix the filling ingredients together and pour into the pastry case (remove the beans first!).
7. Return to oven. Bake at 190°C, gas mark 5 for about 30 min until set and golden on top.

George and Flora added a handful of grated cheese and cooked chopped bacon to theirs.
What would you add? Ham, tomato?
Tip: If you have any pastry left you could make jam tarts.

Mr and Mrs Brown were delighted. They had just run out of eggs.
Their daughter Katy was icing the cakes they had just made.
George and Flora stayed to help.

"These are for my friend Aggie," said Katy. "It's her birthday. Why don't you come and say happy birthday before you go home?"

Katy's Yummy Banana Cup Cakes

Ingredients

Cakes
100 g butter or margarine
100 g caster sugar
2 eggs
100 g self-raising flour
1 ripe banana (mashed)

Plus 12 baking cases, a muffin tin and a toothpick

Icing
200 g icing sugar
100 g softened butter
A few drops of milk

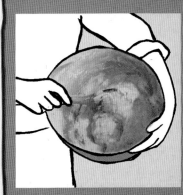

What to do

1. Mix butter and sugar until creamy.
2. Slowly add the beaten eggs.
3. Gently fold in the flour and banana.
4. Spoon mixture into baking cases.
5. Bake at 190°C, gas mark 5 for 15 to 20 min.

   Tip: Check if ready by pushing a toothpick in one. If it comes out clean (not sticky) they are ready.

6. While the cakes cool make the butter icing. Sift the icing sugar and gradually add to the butter and milk, beating until smooth.

Katy has swirled the butter icing and popped a strawberry on top. How would you decorate yours?

Aggie and her brother Matthew were putting out the party food.
There was pizza, sandwiches, feta salad, carrot and celery sticks
and lots of delicious dips.
"Happy birthday!" shouted Katy, George and Flora.

"Thank you," said Aggie. "Have a snack. The carrots came from Dr Kapoor's garden, next door. Shall we take him a cake before you go home?"

Aggie and Matthew's Crunchy Greek Salad and Cool Dip

Feta salad

Ingredients

4 big juicy tomatoes, 1 cucumber, 1 red onion, 1 red pepper

250 g feta cheese

A handful of black olives

Juice of a lemon

75 ml olive oil

Salt and pepper to taste

What to do

1. Cut up the vegetables and cheese into chunks.
2. Mix all the ingredients together in a large bowl.

Tzatziki dip

Ingredients

1 cucumber

450 g pot of strained Greek yoghurt

20 ml olive oil

Juice of half a lemon

1 clove garlic (minced)

A pinch of fresh chopped dill or mint

Salt and pepper to taste

Dipping sticks

Sliced carrot, celery, cucumber, red pepper and pitta bread.

What to do

1. Remove the skin and pips from the cucumber. Finely chop it. Put in a dish with a pinch of salt and pat dry.
2. Mix all the other ingredients, add the cucumber and pop in the fridge.

Tip: For a pizza recipe check out *George and Flora's Secret Garden*, another book in this series.

Dr Kapoor was in his garden.

"We've brought you a cake," said Aggie.

"Thank you and happy birthday," said Dr Kapoor. "I've made some samosas for your party. Would you all like to try one?"

"Oh, yes please," replied Aggie, "and I'd like to introduce you to George and Flora."

Dr Kapoor's Spicy Indian Samosas

Ingredients

Pastry
110 g plain flour
15 ml ghee (or sunflower oil)
40 ml water
Pinch of salt
Note: Makes 10
*Or you can use flour tortillas**
or puff pastry
(Flour tortillas will*
cook slightly quicker.)

Filling
1 clove garlic (crushed)
1 onion (diced)
1 potato (diced)
1 carrot (diced)
Handful of peas
15 ml sunflower oil
2 teaspoons curry powder
(or mixed spices)
100 ml vegetable stock

What to do

Filling

1. Fry onion and garlic until soft.
2. Add other ingredients and fry for 5 min.
3. Add vegetable stock. Cook for 30 min.

Pastry

4. Mix flour and ghee or oil. Add water until you get stiff dough.
5. Divide into 5 balls. Roll into 16 cm circles. Cut in half to make semicircles.
6. Make into a cone, add mixture.
7. Moisten edges with water and press together to seal.
8. Brush with sunflower oil. Put on a greased baking tray and bake at 180°C, gas mark 4, for about 20 min checking and turning about every 7 min.

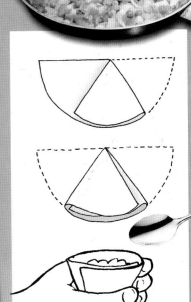

"Hello," said George.
"Nice to meet you, Dr Kapoor,"
added Flora. "The samosas
look delicious. Come on, George,
it really is time we went home."

On their way back, Flora had one of her good ideas.
"Lots of people in our street live close together but don't know each other. Let's invite them all to a big party!" Flora liked parties.

"Brilliant," said George. "Let's have it right here in the street. Let's do invitations for everyone. Grandpa had a street party once. Let's ask him to help."

Feed Grandpa's chickens Friday

George and Flora's to-do list for the party

- Write a list of people to invite.

- Make posters to advertise the party.

- Make invitations for everyone.

- Ask Grandpa which adults we should talk to for help.

- Get a group of adults to help organise it (especially any legal things*) and to help involve everyone.

- Arrange food, drink, music, games, decorations, tables, chairs.

- Make lists of who is doing what including cleaning up afterwards!

* The legal things (in the UK)
You could ask to have a big party in a friend's garden or a community centre or village hall. If you have one in the street, an adult will need to contact the local council (usually at least 12 weeks before). The council may ask you to take out public liability insurance and/or pay a fee. You may also need street party insurance. The Big Lunch website may have some tips: www.thebiglunch.com

Grandpa took George and Flora to meet Mary Smith, the community policewoman, who knew all about organising things.

"What a great idea," said Mary. "My friends at work can help."

"You will both come to the party, won't you?" asked Flora.

Bob's Easy Ice Cream

Inspired by a Caribbean recipe from Bob's mum.

Ingredients

500 ml double cream
80 g icing sugar
*Tip: You could use
300 ml cream and 200 ml
condensed milk*

Flavours

200 g crushed pineapple
and the juice of a lime
Or 200 ml coconut
milk and a handful of
desiccated coconut
Or whatever you fancy:
chocolate, strawberry,
a few drops of vanilla
essence...

What to do

1. Mix all the ingredients (except the cream).
2. Whip the cream until stiff and fold into the mixture.
3. Pop into a container and freeze for at least 4 hours.

Bob sometimes makes 'pass the milk' ice cream. Use a quarter of the amount above and use milk instead of cream. Put in a sealable small tin or freezer bag. Put this into a larger sealable container full of ice and rock salt (10:1), seal that too. Then put on some warm gloves and shake it, play ball, roll it about for 5 to 10 minutes and hey presto – it turns into ice cream.

"Yes, of course we'll come," answered her husband Bob. "We'll make easy ice cream and strawberry kebabs and bring some music. Have you heard of Bob's Band?"

Mary's Frosty Strawberry Kebabs

Ingredients

Fresh strawberries
Melted chocolate, cream
or yoghurt
Wooden kebab sticks

What to do

1. Thread strawberries onto wooden kebab sticks.
2. Put onto a plate. Drizzle with melted chocolate or cream or yoghurt.
3. Freeze.

Bob invited George and Flora to the next band practice
in Sam's garage. George learnt how to play a teapot!
"That was thirsty work," said Sam. "How about some
limeade? Can you stay for Sam's tasty noodles too?"

"Yes please," said **George**. "You will all come to the party, won't you?"

"Yes, of course," they all sang.

"We'll bring the teapot."

Sam's Tasty Thai Noodles

Ingredients

30 ml sunflower oil

1 clove garlic (chopped)

1 fresh red chilli (chopped)

Tip: Wear rubber gloves and/or wash your hands after chopping

2 spring onions (sliced)

Plus a handful of your favourite vegetables (finely sliced): courgette, carrot, red pepper, green beans

A pinch of grated fresh ginger

A pinch of brown sugar

A dash of soy sauce

200 ml coconut milk (optional)

Noodles (to serve with)

Fresh coriander leaves and a slice of lime to garnish

What to do

1. Fry the garlic and chilli in the oil for 2 min.

2. Add the other vegetables and ginger. Fry for 1 min.

3. Add sugar, soy sauce and coconut milk. Cook for 5 min.

4. Serve with noodles and garnish with coriander and lime.

Sam's Tangy Limeade

Ingredients

5 limes (washed)

120 g sugar (or to taste)

600 ml boiling water

What to do

1. Squeeze out the lime juice.

2. Put the skins and sugar in a jug. Add boiling water.

3. Leave for 20 min to cool.

4. Strain, add lime juice. Cool in fridge.

George went to see Grandpa's friend Stefan to invite him to the party.
"Hello," said Stefan. "Meet my grandchildren; Jake, Hugh, Jack, Martha,
Charlie, Ruby and Meg."
"Hello," said George. "Grandpa says you might have some ideas for the big party."
"Yes," laughed Stefan. "We certainly know how to feed lots of people."

"You will all come to the party, won't you?" asked Grandpa.

"Oh yes," they shouted.

"We'll bring a huge potato bake and masses of bean stew."

Stefan's Scrumptious Bean Stew and Potato Bake

Inspired by Stefan's Polish family recipes

Potato Bake

Ingredients

Butter or margarine (for greasing the tin)

500 g par-boiled (half cooked) potatoes (cubed)

1 onion (chopped and fried for 3 min)

1 egg (beaten)

100 ml milk and sour cream (50:50)

What to do

1. Put potatoes and cooked onion in a greased baking dish.

2. Mix milk, cream and egg and pour over the potatoes.

3. Bake at 180°C, gas mark 4 for about an hour.

Bean Stew

Ingredients

15 ml sunflower oil

1 clove garlic and 1 red onion (chopped)

1 potato, 1 carrot, 1 parsnip, 1 leek, 1 squash (peeled and chopped)

400 g cooked tinned beans (white, black eye or mixed)

200 g chopped, cooked bacon or Polish sausage (Kielbasa) (both optional)

400 g tin of tomatoes

200 ml vegetable stock or 2 teaspoons Vegeta (Polish seasoning) mixed in 200 ml hot water

A pinch of paprika and of oregano

What to do

1. Fry the garlic and onion in the oil. 2 min.

2. Add and fry the other vegetables. 5 min.

3. Add the rest of the ingredients. Cover with a lid. Simmer on the hob or bake in the oven for 1 hour stirring occasionally (add more liquid if necessary).

Tip: Stefan puts a spoonful of sour cream and chopped parsley on the top when he serves up. Serves up to 8.

Mum, Flora and baby Daisy called in to give Mrs Taylor her invitation. Mrs Taylor made tea and gave them a special treat she used to cook for her own children before they grew up and moved away.

"Cheesy owl, anyone?"

"Yes please," said Flora. "You will come to the party, won't you?"

Mrs Taylor's Cheesy Owls

Ingredients

Use Grandpa's pastry recipe
150 g cheese
1 egg yolk
Decorating: Black olives, carrot, pepper, sesame and cumin seeds

What to do

1. At the breadcrumbs stage - add 150 g grated cheese and an egg yolk.

2. Mix together adding water until it forms a stiff dough.

3. Roll out, cut into circles, pinch two ears.

4. Put on a greased baking tray.

5. Decorate with sliced olives for eyes, a carrot or red pepper beak and sesame or cumin seeds for the speckled tummy feathers.

6. Bake at 200°C, gas mark 6, for about 20 min until set and golden.

"Yes, I would love to come," said Mrs Taylor. "I'll make some bunting and bring cheesy owls."

It was June and the big day arrived.
The sun shone, the band played and everyone
in the street came out and joined the party.

At the end of the day everyone went home tired, happy and with a whole load of new friends.

"That was a **BIG** party," said George.

"That was a **GREAT** party," said Flora.

"Let's start planning next year's."

"We'll help!" shouted the neighbours.

Roll on the next party. We're writing a new song for it. Matthew has joined the band.
Thanks guys,
Bob's Band

Dear George and Flora,
We're going to do cooking classes at the new community centre. Can you teach us how to make pastry?
Thanks
Aggie and Matthew

Fabulous party. Mrs Taylor and I are off to our first dance class together tonight.
Best wishes and thank you,
Stefan

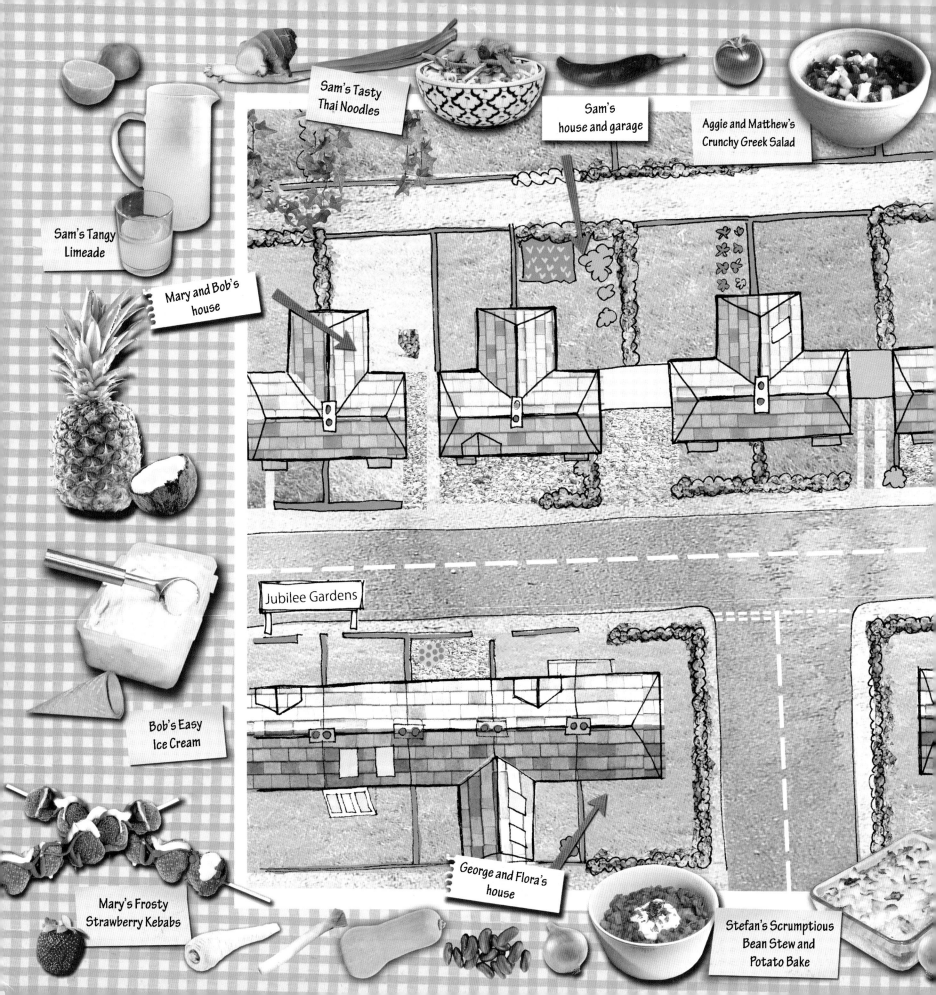

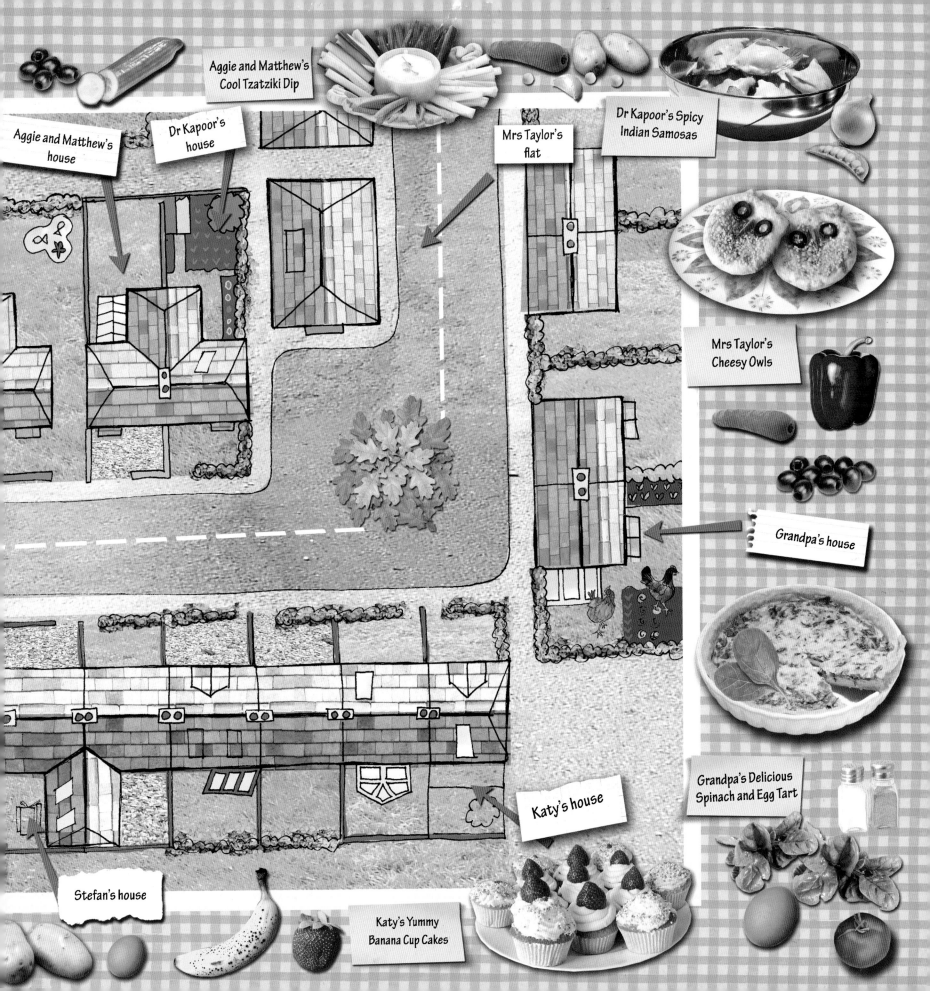

Aggie and Matthew's Cool Tzatziki Dip

Aggie and Matthew's house

Dr Kapoor's house

Mrs Taylor's flat

Dr Kapoor's Spicy Indian Samosas

Mrs Taylor's Cheesy Owls

Grandpa's house

Grandpa's Delicious Spinach and Egg Tart

Katy's house

Stefan's house

Katy's Yummy Banana Cup Cakes

Read all the adventures of George and Flora:

The Eden Project

The Eden Project, an educational charity in Cornwall, built a global garden in a massive crater that once used to be a china clay pit. Eden creates gardens, exhibitions, events and projects that explore how people can work together, care for the natural world and change things for the better.

www.edenproject.com

The Big Lunch

The Big Lunch is one of Eden's projects. It encourages people across the UK and beyond to get together with their neighbours for a few hours of community, friendship and fun. The Eden Project started The Big Lunch because it believes that we are better equipped to tackle challenges when we face them together.

www.thebiglunch.com

   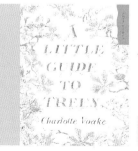 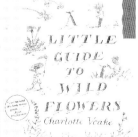